improving garden soil with **GREEN MANURES** *a guide for the home gardener*

by Richard Alther and Richard O. Raymond

i

CONTENTS

INTRODUCTION

Chemical fertilizers are a relatively recent food growing device, not widely used until the current century. Leaving land "fallow" or unseeded for a season or two was one important way to restore nutrient balance. Rotation of crops was devised as a way to replenish organic matter and nutrients without skipping an annual crop. Nitrogen-consuming corn and nitrogen-fixing clover, for example, were often rotated.

Green manuring — the growing and turning under of foliage crops solely for their fertilizing and soil conditioning values — is even a more rapid and effective method of soil management, practiced for centuries but much less common in today's agriculture.

Certainly the farmer is not to be faulted for choosing chemical fertilizers in his often losing battle to stay on the land. But with quickly dwindling world supplies of mineable phosphorus and other ingredients of costly chemical fertilizers, green manuring is bound to gain wide popularity and importance.

The growing of green manures is especially suited for the gardener who is planning on growing food indefinitely in the same location. His concern for proper replenishing of the soil is concentrated in just a patch, compared to the farmer's vast acreage.

The gardener has a great opportunity to turn just about any piece of soil that gets decent sun and drainage into "textbook" loam. Over the course of several years, adding more to the topsoil than he takes away as harvested crops, a gardener can be rewarded with all the vigorous, fairly pest-resistant fruits and vegetables he could possibly use.

Green manuring is a way to build up and maintain soil for *any* gardener, with or without powered equipment. But we should stress at this point that a rear-mounted rotary tiller is by far the easiest and fastest method possible.

Rotary tillage, as opposed to plowing and harrowing with large farm equipment, can incorporate more air and nitrogen into soil, critical for the leguminous, nitrogen-fixing green manures. Specifically, rotary tillers with rear-end tines can finely chop up and turn under organic material to hasten the benefits of green manuring.

We would like to gratefully acknowledge the use of the research and photographs of one particular rotary tiller company that has pioneered green manuring in this country. Troy-Bilt Roto Tiller-Power Composters, manufactured in Troy, N.Y., are the descendants of the original Rototiller Corporation of Troy, which introduced rotary tillage to the United States from Europe almost thirty years ago. They published a book on growing green manures in 1949 called "Power Gardening and Power Composting."

There are other makes of similar tines-in-the-rear machines in this country, in England and elsewhere, which will do comparable work. They are not as widely distributed as the Troy-Bilt and are more expensive, but this situation may change as the demand increases for machines designed for green manuring.

Whether or not you feel alternatives to chemical fertilizers are timely, we hope you will consider green manuring for its soil conditioning benefits alone. They are substantial.

Soft, dark, humus-rich soil.

IMPROVING GARDEN SOIL
WITH GREEN MANURE

The importance of adding organic matter to your soil each year . . .

Your soil is alive! And if you want it to be healthy, fertile, and continuously productive, it must be fed plenty of organic matter.

By "alive" we specifically mean that each square inch of good garden soil contains teeming *millions* of micro-organisms, each with a different but vital function that in combination regulates soil fertility. Most forms of soil life are too small to see. Of course, we're all familiar with the largest variety — the ordinary earthworm — which feeds entirely upon raw, undigested vegetable (organic) matter.

In the gradual process of literally eating and decomposing organic wastes, like leaves and all dead plant and animal remains, the soil life causes the release of the valuable minerals and trace elements *so that they can be used again as plant nutrients in a form that roots can absorb.*

In addition to its fertilizing effects, all this organic material greatly benefits the *texture* of any soil. It binds together overly loose, sandy soil, and crumbles and loosens hard-packed, clay-like soil.

You've heard the term "humus", which is organic matter at its final stage of decomposition. Humus gives a good soil its important spongy texture. It allows the necessary circulation of air to the plant roots and soil.

Humus gives soil its ability to absorb and retain just the right amount of moisture, too.

Without continuously fueling the soil with organic matter, it can truly become lifeless and unable to support plants. Earthworms, which are ravenous eaters, will go elsewhere in search of food. Minerals and other nutrients will stay "locked up" in soil particles, unavailable for plant growth without the intense activity of micro-organisms (microbes, for short).

Decomposing organic matter produces weak carbonic acids which help to dissolve soil nutrients. This is just another of so many important "missions" of soil organic matter that come to a halt when fresh supplies are unavailable. Insect pests and disease organisms take over what weak and vulnerable growth can be produced. Chemical fertilizers can be poured on in huge quantities, but unfortunately they don't do a thing for the soil texture and a flourishing soil life population in the long run.

Perhaps today the most beneficial aspect of adding organic matter to our garden soils is re-cycling wastes that would otherwise stimulate plant growth where it's *not* needed — in our waterways.

These statements oversimplify a very complex cycle of nature, which is far better explained in textbooks and environmental publications. But hopefully they give a general idea of just *how essential* are regular and generous additions of organic matter to any garden soil.

There are many ways to obtain organic matter and ways to mix it into your soil. Here are the most common methods:

1. You can go out and buy it in packaged form. Peat moss, dehydrated manures, even sewage sludge, can be hauled to your garden, used first as a mulch, and then finally worked in. (Mulching spreads organic matter around your plants in a thick enough layer to suffocate weed growth, conserve soil moisture, and insulate the ground so that earthworms and other soil organisms can stay active during warm weather.)

2. You can (and *should*) chop and till all garden residues and weeds into your soil after the crop is finished bearing.

3. You can also buy bales of hay or straw, use it for mulching, then chop and till it into the soil.

4. You can obtain and use wood shavings or wastes from canneries, cider mills, and other local processors, usually free for the taking. (Use wood products where you want an acid soil and a slow-decomposing mulch.)

5. You can often get permission to mow weeds (preferably *green* and free of seeds) and hay from nearby fields to use as mulch.

6. You can gather leaves to be chopped and tilled in.

7. You can use all kinds of animal manures, household garbage, yard and lawn clippings.

8. You can collect *all* of the above materials and compost them in heaps, possibly shredding them first, and *then* work into your garden the finished organic product.

9. You can grow crops as "green manure", strictly for their soil-improving benefits, to be chopped and tilled into the soil right where they stand while growing (or grown and cut, to be used as mulch at a different location in the garden).

This book is about the growing of green manure crops, either as a protective topsoil cover crop or as a good source of mulch material. In both cases, the green manure is eventually chopped up and mixed into the soil as a valuable fertilizer and soil conditioner. Soft, dark, "spongy" soil is abundant in organic matter in various stages of decomposition. It quickly absorbs hard rains and stays moist in dry spells. It has a pleasant and rich *smell* to it.

HERE'S HOW TO DO IT

1. Why Green Manure Crops are, perhaps, the very easiest and fastest way to improve garden soil

By "fast" we don't mean in just one season. If your soil has been neglected for many years, it will most likely take more than one year to restore it completely to a productive, fertile state. Nature does things gradually, but there are some things that the gardener can do in order to create ideal conditions and give nature a boost.

Growing green manures is an outstanding technique for improving soil texture with added humus content and building up the available supply of topsoil plant nutrients because it is a faster version of what happens in nature anyway. Plants grow by drawing nutrients from the soil, die, and then return to the earth those nutrients that were used in growing. Unless used as a source for mulch material, which will be discussed later, green manures are crops grown simply for the purpose of being chopped and mixed directly back into the soil. They feed the earthworms and soil organisms, which in turn stimulate and speed up the whole process of releasing nutrients and making them available to plants. They utilize otherwise wasted solar energy by creating green material. You end up with a larger, more active soil life population, greatly increased organic matter content, and a more highly fertile soil.

A friend recently chose a garden site badly overlooked for years. It was too sandy and needed lots of organic matter for water retention. After one plowing and sowing of buckwheat, at least topsoil erosion and weed growth were checked.

When the buckwheat had bloomed, it was chopped and tilled into the soil, adding many tons of fresh organic matter. This is certainly easier and faster than most any other method we know. Then, too, many green manure crops have nice long roots which "tap" deep-buried nutrients and trace minerals — needed in small amounts but very necessary — that surface-applied methods don't always furnish.

The following summary of advantages of green manuring explains specifically *how* these crops tremendously improve soil fertility and texture.

2. The many advantages of growing Green Manures in any soil:

First of all, with green manuring you can avoid the time and work of collecting and hauling organic matter to your garden. You can grow it in large amounts right where you want it.

• Green manure is a very economical source of organic matter, unlike animal manures, if you can even find them to buy. Green manures are also easy to add to your soil, if you have the proper tools. From there, you can let the earthworms and other soil life make "manure" out of the green matter you're feeding them.

• A lush green manure crop keeps your garden attractive right up to snow cover. You'll enjoy looking at it, and so will your neighbors.

• When left over winter, a green manure is primarily a "cover crop" in that it protects the soil surface from erosion from harsh winter winds, snow storms, and quick thaws. You work hard to build up precious topsoil, and this is the best way to conserve it. The green plant material is like a temporary "storehouse" of nutrients so they can't be washed away. Obviously, you maximize the values of green manuring by turning it under while still growing — *before* winter. Although earthworms continue to feed on the roots and near-to-surface stems, a crop left over winter serves mainly as cover and erosion control.

• Green manure acts as an insulating blanket and keeps the soil warmer in winter, cooler in summer. This greatly encourages earthworms and soil life activity in general. Rapid freezing and thawing of unprotected soil works against a gardener's efforts. The freezing action breaks down soil aggregates and causes compaction, the opposite of what you want.

• The more earthworms are sheltered by and eventually fed with turned-under green manures, the more channels they'll burrow deep in the subsoil and the more minerals and nutrients they'll return to the surface.

• The roots of many green manure crops as well as weeds (which are left to grow as green manure) reach deep into the *subsoil*, absorbing and bringing up valuable nutrients into the plant tissue, which then will revitalize the *topsoil*.

• When the crop is turned under, the decaying roots contribute a large amount of organic matter themselves. So, humus content, soil life, water retention, and air circulation improve all the way down.

• Certain crops called "legumes" have the ability to capture and fix large amounts of nitrogen from the air, actually adding *more* of this important plant nutrient to the soil when tilled under than they consumed in growing. The common legumes are peas, beans, alfalfa, and clovers. More on this later.

• Depending upon your specific soil profile, by growing green manures you can cut down on your need to purchase fertilizers and other soil additives and conditioners.

With the world's supply of topsoil being rapidly exhausted, every gardener (and farmer, if possible) owes it to his land and future generations to restore soil humus content and maintain fertility. It is estimated that in the U.S. alone one million acres is paved over each year, so the increasing shortage of tillable land gets worse. And our average percentage of organic matter content is down to about 1.5% from a minimum recommended level of 5% and an ideal of 10% to 12%, as in virgin topsoil. A continuous cover of rye grasses grown in parts of a garden when idle, is an easy and sensible plan for every gardener. After several seasons of green manuring, a garden, formerly a worn-out pasture, measures over 10% organic matter content.

• Since the growing of green manures means turning under harvested crop residues, you are performing many constructive steps as a result. Your soil gets the extra benefit of all that good organic matter when the residues are incorporated. Most importantly, tilling under residues destroys the winter shelter and food supply and breeding grounds for corn borers, cutworms of all kinds, and many other garden insect pests which live on specific plants. Some plant disease organisms are also largely prevented from carrying over to the next season, deprived of their appropriate host.

● The growing of green manure crops means additional tillings of the soil. This brings more weed seeds to the surface to either germinate and be killed by a subsequent tilling in season, or die of exposure to the cold in early spring or late fall. And a soft garden soil, conditioned with green manures, makes it easier to pull those weeds, roots and all, when you do want to get rid of them!

● A green manure garden becomes more and more weed-free as a result of this work, *and* because the crop simply chokes out weeds so they can't get a head start on you.

● Keep idle parts of your garden busy growing a green manure crop, and you're capturing and using the sun's energy to make organic matter, constantly replenishing the soil between your cultivated, harvested crops. Remember, your garden cannot stay fertile and productive very long unless for every bit of harvest you take out of it, you put something good for it right back in the soil.

● Green manuring saves time and work for gardeners who haul materials to a compost pile, and layer, turn, water, and wait for them to become the finished product. Fresh green manures can be chopped up and tilled under at their maximum growth, yet before they get *tough*. Then, they not only break down faster in the soil, but provide much more nutritious and tender food for the earthworms. *And,* half the value of the organic matter *isn't lost through leaching,* as it is in a compost pile.

● This next and final advantage is for the gardener himself. To someone for whom gardening is the favorite of all activities, green manuring extends the active, outdoor season from early spring to late fall. After the main crops of fruits and vegetables are done, you can grow green manures in the cool, invigorating weeks of autumn. It's a great feeling to be doing something *good* for your soil.

3. The basic step-by-step procedure of sowing your green manure crop:

Timing; when to start

If your soil is so poor that you want to begin as soon as possible, you can sow an appropriate green manure crop at *any* time during the growing season. A section follows shortly, discussing the specific varieties you can use.

But if you want to garden in a particular spot and see what vegetables and fruits you can successfully produce, go ahead. Then you can embark on a green manure plan in the late summer and see how your food crops progress each year thereafter with the soil gradually but steadily improving.

If you have plenty of land with good sun exposure and drainage, then perhaps you'll want to grow food crops in one part and begin improving another part with continuous green manures. Each year you could rotate your food crops and green manures, and this would be ideal.

Chop and turn under the still-green crop residues.

For now, we'll assume you don't have room for rotation and just want to improve your garden soil in its current location.

All residues should go preferably back into the soil before you can sow a green manure crop. The very *best* thing you can do for your soil is to chop up and turn under those residues when they're still young, green, and tender — the sooner after harvest the better. Then they're that much more succulent to the earthworms and microbes, *and* they break down much faster. You could get a jump on green manuring by sowing seeds after your final cultivation, between rows of plants, later turning under the crop residues *and* some green manure.

Provided you have a suitable tiller, it's very easy to turn under all kinds of residues — tomato and pea vines, thick roots, even standing cornstalks. Surrounded by air, moisture, and hungry microbes, residues decompose much quicker in the soil than they can in a separate compost pile.

A good chance to end the weed cycle. Weeds as well as the residues can be turned into the topsoil. With a rear-tine rotary tiller it takes two or perhaps three passes over to get the organic matter well chopped and buried. You should wait from three to ten days, depending upon the weather, and till again before sowing green manure seeds, so that residues will be well decomposed and soil nutrients won't be monopolized by the microbial activity. The extra tilling will destroy weeds and weed seeds and incorporate added oxygen for speedier decomposition, as well.

Hand composting. If you are gardening entirely by hand, without power equipment, then you most likely would want to reduce your garden residues in a separate compost pile. Tender wastes eventually can turn into humus, and the tough fibers at least will be partially broken — enough so to make reasonable the work of spading under by hand.

A nice, fine seedbed is the next step. Your garden is now clear of crop residues and ready to prepare as a fall seedbed. Most green manure seeds are on the small side, so the seedbed should be groomed fine for them to make contact with the soil. This will speed germination and get the crop off to an early start.

Good time to add lime. If you didn't get a chance last spring to add some ground limestone, now is a good opportunity. Most soil is in need of a lime application only once every three years. A soil test is one way to judge more accurately the amount needed. Lime will not interfere with the green manure seeds you're about to plant. Lime can be lightly broadcast by hand, then tilled into the topsoil surface.

Fertilizer, too. One of the disadvantages if gardeners use commercial fertilizer is over-stimulating foliage and green growth in food crops at the expense of the fruit. This is exactly what you *do* want in starting a green manure crop. Especially if you've had a very poor gardening season on neglected soil, a light application of 10-10-10 fertilizer will boost the growth of the green manure and at least will assure an ample harvest of

Green Manure seed is hand-broadcast sparingly.

organic matter. You could spread and till this in at the same time you apply the ground limestone. We also recommend you take a soil test to determine specific fertilizer and liming requirements.

Hand-broadcasting seed. The easiest way to sow the seeds of your green manure cover crop is by hand,

broadcast style. Just make sure you don't get too "heavy-handed" and sow too thickly. Like any crop, it will grow fastest if reasonably spaced apart. See the guide on pages 22 and 23 for specific recommended amounts for each variety.

Cover as you would a new lawn. Next the seed is lightly covered with fine soil. This can be done with a rear-mounted rotary tiller, or you could do this essential step by hand with a rake, just as you would plant a new lawn.

The chart of green manures information on pages 22 and 23 lists specific planting depths for each variety. Tramping or rolling will hasten germination, as will watering, if conditions are dry.

Green cover of rye is up in a few weeks.

Up and growing. In a few weeks a green manure crop of ryegrass will be a light green blanket of grass and roots, which will do much good for your garden even if it only grows a few inches before winter sets in. The tight web of roots already will be sufficient to hold the soil securely and stop erosion that could result from wind and rain. It will also prevent needless evaporation of moisture from uncovered soil.

Next spring. As the snow melts from a northern garden, a thick matting of dead ryegrass remains the following spring. It's all ready to be chopped up and spaded or tilled under when the soil has warmed up sufficiently. Already the dead and decomposed blades of grass and roots are providing food for the earthworms.

A perennial crop grows again. If you had used a perennial crop, such as a rye which survives the winter, then

Dead annual rye is ready next spring to till under.

you would allow it to grow up again before tilling under to get a double helping of organic matter. Since it's best to till under *any* kind of organic material well before planting (ten days to two weeks), this space in the garden will have to be reserved for a late-planted crop, such as sweet corn.

4. The most common kinds of Green Manure Cover Crops for home use:

A. Ryegrass. The hardy one with lush, rapid green growth, ryegrass is easy to grow and yields abundant green matter. It will take hold in almost any soil, anywhere in the country. It also is easy to find in farm supply stores. We recommend the *annual* type for most purposes, which will survive only until the heavy freezes of winter. It's ideal for the first-to-plant section of the garden, since next spring the grass and roots will be dead, partially decomposed, and easily turned under.

If you plant the *perennial* or permanent variety of ryegrass, called winter rye, it can survive the winter and yield another harvest of green growth in the spring. By tilling under, the roots and all are completely shredded and buried and won't return to interfere with your next crop. For hand gardeners or with front-end tillers, it would be better to use just the annual ryegrass.

B. Buckwheat grows even in the poorest soil, and so fast that it chokes out weeds.

It's hard to beat buckwheat as a green manure for really impoverished soil. It will grow in sand, clay, overly dry or wet areas. Of course, it will be scraggly and reflect the low soil quality, but at least you can get a cover crop going. Buckwheat can be seeded by hand in the ordinary broadcast manner.

Hardy buckwheat pleases the bees, too.

Like rye, the advantage of buckwheat as a green manure is the production of a lot of organic material very quickly. It's especially wonderful for loosening up tough sod and killing it when you're making a brand new garden.

Buckwheat is much hardier than most of the other grains, such as wheat, corn, and oats. It's particularly good in the northeast United States, but don't hesitate to try it in the other sections of the country, too.

Buckwheat actually is an in-season summer green manure for soil improvement. It's best to sow it when the ground is thoroughly warmed in summertime, say in June or July, after you've harvested your peas and other early crops. It will reach the blossom stage in about six to eight weeks and be ready for harvesting as a mulch, chicken feed, or, a little later when seeds are fully mature, for your own buckwheat flour.

You'll be finding honey bees swarming through buckwheat blossoms. Pollen is often hard to find at that time of year, and the bees love it. It makes a wonderfully rich, dark honey. The buckwheat grows so thick that weeds, old sod, and other growth literally are suffocated.

In late summer a rear-end rotary tiller can be used to chop up and turn under a hip-high growth of buckwheat. A better alternative to turning under your buckwheat crop is to simply mow it down and leave it.

Harvest buckwheat for mulch or later to make your own flour.

The seeds will settle in the loosened soil and replant the crop the following spring. This way you can get two green manure crops from a single sowing, if your soil really needs improving and if you can wait that long before planting a food crop. Caution: to get rid of buckwheat permanently, be sure to till it under after blossoming but *before* the seeds develop.

C. The Legumes have the unique ability to "fix" valuable nitrogen from the air, greatly enriching soil fertility.

The green manures just discussed are categorized as grasses and grains. Another plant crop group is called legumes, and they have a very special importance when used for soil improvement. Legumes attract certain types of microbes in the soil to their roots which extract nitrogen from the air and convert it to usable form for the plants. So a legume actually returns more nitrogen to the soil than it used in growing — a real bonus as a soil-improving green manure.

To make sure the nitrogen-fixing microbes are present, it's usually recommended to "inoculate" legume seeds with a mixture of these tiny creatures before planting. The inoculant culture, which comes like a dark powder from most suppliers of legume seeds, is mixed with water according to the directions and evenly coats the seeds.

Perennial hairy vetch is a slow starter.

A perennial clover is a plus also for beekeepers.

You'll find a long list of common green manures, legumes, and non-legumes listed in the chart on pages 22 and 23. Hairy vetch — one of the many types of vetch — is perennial, but relatively slow growing. It's good to plant a fast-growing annual "nurse crop" like rye or oats along with the inoculated vetch seed to provide shade and check competitive weed growth. If you do this, though, plant the perennial more thinly than you would ordinarily. Otherwise the annual nurse crop may be choked out by the sturdy perennial.

There are many kinds of perennial clover, and most likely there is one well suited to your climate. The blossoms are ideal for honey bees. With both vetch and clover, you should plan to allow the crop to grow at least one full season, perhaps two, to get the maximum benefit from nitrogen fixation and green growth. Alsike clover has the benefit of growing on ground too wet for the red clovers. One disadvantage of vetch and clover, however, is that they're wiry and sometimes difficult to destroy completely if left for several years.

Many common vegetables are legumes, so you can get both food and green manure from the same crop. They include all of the bean and pea families. As you probably have found, it takes a lot of garden peas to harvest enough for your family. They're so very delicious that they don't go far. Well, you can really stretch the garden pea harvest and almost get the effect of a cover crop by planting the seeds broadcast style in very wide rows. This way they'll choke out competitive weeds and keep the ground moist and cool, too.

15

Like other legumes, peas add much nitrogen.

You can get away with close-crop planting of peas in most soils because they're so hardy. And as legumes they produce helpful amounts of the plant nutrient nitrogen. Seeds may be planted between two parallel strings in a foot-and-a-half wide band. Then a rotary tiller is run over the row in very shallow depth, enough to cover and bury the seeds with an inch or so of topsoil.

Cowpeas are a fast-growing variety for green manuring purposes. Peas are excellent for green manure because they produce so much foliage. Try sowing them in combination with oats to help support the vines.

Another good edible legume is the common soybean, increasingly more important as a true meat substitute. Soybeans are the only vegetable which has the essential proteins of meat. A crop of soybeans like this can be grown strictly as green manure, too, and greatly improve the soil in just one season. Also, soybeans stand more drought than peas.

Alfalfa is another very well-known legume, grown ex-

Soybeans have great table value, too, for their protein.

tensively throughout the country as high-protein forage for livestock. Alfalfa really needs a year or two to get full benefit from its long, penetrating roots, which can reach 18 to 20 feet. If you've got the extra room for alfalfa, it's certainly worth it. Actually, alfalfa offers so very many advantages as green manure, we'll discuss it later in a special section.

Can you guess a strange green manure cover crop? You're right, it's weeds! Called "the guardians of the soil", they must not be overlooked as the most common green manure Mother Nature uses at all times. Weeds help to adjust and correct for nutrient and trace mineral imbalances in a soil. Most weeds are very deep-rooted and draw up valuable elements to the topsoil. We think of them as a nuisance in competing with food crops, but in an idle section of garden they're busily at work for you, if only in keeping the topsoil covered and intact. Just till them under before they go to seed, especially if you plan food crops there the next year.

17

Kale flourishes under just about any conditions.

Kale: the Winter Wonder Crop.

A lot of people have never tasted freshly-picked kale. It happens to be an amazing crop for all of these reasons: It's very easy to grow; bugs don't bother it very much; you can plant it anytime from early spring to late fall (this picture taken in early September); it can be sown as a cover crop; it does everything for your soil that a good thick non-leguminous green manure crop should do; frost helps to *improve* the flavor; you can actually dig it out of the snow in the dead of winter; *and* it can be picked anytime and provides delicious greens cooked like spinach or served raw in salads.

Winter picking of kale is an unusual experience but very simple. The kale stays crisp and delicious right under the snow, shown here being uncovered. Kale is extremely high in vitamin A. If you haven't tried kale in your garden, you'll most likely be pleased if you do.

Quite often the kale survives the winter and keeps growing another crop of greens like this one, the following spring. Finally, the crop can be tilled back under, adding more valuable organic matter.

D. Alfalfa, the "King of Soil Improvement crops", is great if you've got the room to spare.

From all the research we've been able to do ourselves

Alfalfa often is the best green manure of all.

and accumulate on the subject, it seems that alfalfa is number one when it comes to green manures. U.S. agriculture realizes the value of alfalfa. It is estimated that over one-third of all the hay produced in our country is now alfalfa.

Alfalfa is right on the top in terms of protein content, which breaks down into usable nitrate fertilizer. It's mostly grown as the most palatable and nutritious food for livestock, so it's an unexpected delicacy for the earthworms.

If you'd like to take advantage of this fertile green manure, you can either plant alfalfa and let it grow for at least two seasons in a large part of your garden (to get the benefit of its long roots breaking up and "mining" the subsoil) or you can grow it in a permanent spot nearby and harvest it as mulch.

Alfalfa is a legume, so it has all the many advantages of hosting nitrogen-fixing bacteria on its roots and greatly enhancing the soil's fertility.

Alfalfa has very long roots, up to twenty feet. They penetrate deep into the subsoil, as do full-grown trees, searching out moisture if needed and a whole array of

essential major and minor plant nutrients. When the crop is eventually turned under, these roots add a wealth of organic matter, conditioning and improving the soil far beyond the reach of normal plants and regular tillage.

Alfalfa is high in nitrogen, considerably higher than most legumes. So as a green manure, its leaves and stalks have stored up many more nutrients than they used in growing.

Alfalfa also contains the other valuable nutrients of calcium, magnesium, phosphorus, potassium, manganese, and zinc, which make it a nearly complete

natural fertilizer. Livestock fed alfalfa require much less feed supplement than they would ordinarily need.

Alfalfa makes the most valuable mulch, especially when it's harvested the second or third time in a season, because it's practically weed-free.

Alfalfa simply does all the things an outstanding green manure cover crop should do towards making a soil easily workable and rich in nutrients. For all these reasons you'll certainly want to include it in your green manuring plans if at all possible.

Common Name		Legume	Soil Preference	Lime Requirements (Low, Medium or High)	Adapted to Soils of Low Fertility	Relative Longevity of Seed	Seeding Rate (lbs. per acre)	Seeding Rate (lbs. per 1000 sq. ft.)	Depth to Cover Seed	N.E. and N.C. States	Southern and S.E. States	Gulf Coast and Florida	Northwestern States	Southwestern States	When to Sow	When to Turn Under	Comments
Barley		No	Loams	L		Long	100	2½	¾	•			•	•	Spring / Fall	Summer / Spring	Not good on sandy or acid soils. Sow spring varieties in north, winter varieties in milder climates.
Beans	Mung	Yes	Widely Adaptable	L	•	Short	70	2	1		•	•		•	Spring or Summer	Summer or Fall	Warm weather crops. Do not sow until ground is warm and weather is settled.
	Soy	Yes	Loams	M		Short	90	2½	1½		•	•	•	•	Spring or Summer	Summer or Fall	
	Velvet	Yes	Loams	L	•	Short	120	4	2			•			Spring or Summer	Summer or Fall	
Beggar Weed		Yes	Sandy Loams	L			15	½	½			•			Spring or Early Summer	Summer or Fall	Seeding rate is for scarified seed. Treble the amount if unhulled seed is used.
Brome Grass, Field		No	Widely Adaptable	L		Long	30	1	½	•					Fall / Spring	Spring / Fall	Good winter cover. Easy to establish. Hardier than rye. More heat tolerant.
Buckwheat		No	Widely Adaptable	L	•		50	1½	¾	•			•		Late Spring and Summer	Summer or Fall	Quick growing. Plant only after ground is warm.
Bur Clover		Yes	Heavy Loams	M		Long	30	1	½		•	•		•	Fall	Spring	Not winter hardy north. One of the best winter crops where mild winters prevail.
Chess or Cheat Grass		No	Loams	L		Long	40	1	¾					•	Fall	Spring	
Clover	Alsike	Yes	Heavy Loams	M		Long	8	¼	½				•	•	Spring / Fall	Fall / Spring	Less sensitive to soil acidity and poorly drained soils than most clovers.
	Crimson	Yes	Loams	M	•	Medium	30	1	½	•	•	•		•	Fall / Spring	Spring / Fall	Not winter hardy north. A good winter annual from New Jersey southward.
	Subterranean	Yes	Loams	M		Medium	30	1	½					•	Fall	Spring	
Corn		No	Widely Adaptable	L		Medium	90	2½	1	•	•	•		•	Spring or Summer	Summer or Fall	Do not sow until ground is warm.
Cow-Pea		Yes	Sandy Loams	L	•	Short	90	2½	1½					•	Late Spring or Early Summer	Summer or Fall	Withstands drought and moderate shade well. Do not sow until weather is warm and settled.
Crotalaria		Yes	Light Loams	L	•	Long	15	½	¾			•			Spring or Summer	Summer or Fall	Does well on acid soils. Resistant to root knot nematode. Sow scarified seed.
Fenugreek		Yes	Loams	L		Long	35	1	½					•	Fall	Spring	
Guar		Yes	Widely Adaptable	L	•	Long	40	1½	1					•	Spring or Early Summer	Summer or Fall	Thrives on warm soils. Do not plant too early.
Indigo, Hairy		Yes	Sandy Loams	L	•	Short	10	½	½		•	•		•	Spring or Early Summer	Summer or Fall	
Kale, Scotch		No	Widely Adaptable	H	•	Long	14	¼	½	•	•	•	•	•	Summer or Fall	Spring	Can be eaten after serving as winter cover. In Northern areas interplant with winter rye for protection. Except in deep south, plant in summer for good growth before frost.
Lespedeza	Common	Yes	Loams	L	•	Short	25	1	½		•				Early Spring	Summer or Fall	Easy to establish on hard, badly eroded soils. / Good on acid soils of low fertility.
	Korean	Yes	Loams	L	•	Short	25	1	½		•				Early Spring	Summer or Fall	
	Sericea	Yes	Loams	L	•	Medium	25	1	½		•			•	Early Spring	Summer or Fall	
Lupine	Blue	Yes	Sandy Loams	L		Short	100	2½	1			•			Spring / Fall	Summer / Spring	Less popular than the yellow lupine and blue lupine. / Good on sour and acid soils.
	White	Yes	Sandy Loams	L		Short	120	2½	1	•		•			Spring / Fall	Summer / Spring	
	Yellow	Yes	Sandy Loams	L		Short	80	2	1	•		•			Spring / Fall	Summer / Spring	
Millet		No	Sandy Loams	L		Long	30	1	½	•					Late Spring or Summer	Summer or Fall	Sow only after ground is warm, a week or ten days after normal corn planting time. Fast growing.
Mustard, White		No	Loams				8	¼	¼	•					Spring	Summer	

NURE INFORMATION

Common Name		Legume	Soil Preference	Lime Requirements (Low, Medium or High)	Adapted to Soils of Low Fertility	Relative Longevity of Seed	Seeding Rate (lbs. per acre)	Seeding Rate (lbs. per 1000 sq. ft.)	Depth to Cover Seed	N.E. and N.C. States	Southern and S.E. States	Gulf Coast and Florida	Northwestern States	Southwestern States	When to Sow	When to Turn Under	Comments
Oats		No	Widely Adaptable	L		Long	100	2½	1	•	•	•	•	•	Spring / Fall	Summer or Fall / Spring	Winter oats (sown in fall) are suitable only where mild winters prevail.
Pea	Field	Yes	Heavy Loams	M		Short	90	2½	1½	•	•	•	•	•	Early Spring / Fall	Summer / Spring	Sow in fall only where winters are mild. Distinctly a cool weather crop.
	Rough	Yes	Sandy Loams	L	•	Medium	60	1½	1		•				Fall	Spring	
	Tangier	Yes		M		Medium	80	2½	1	•				•	Spring	Summer	
Rape		No	Loams	L			8	¼	¼	•			•		Spring or Summer	Summer or Fall	
Rescue Grass		No	Widely Adaptable	L		Long	35	1	¾		•		•				Adapted to mild winters and humid climates.
Rye, Spring		No	Widely Adaptable	L		Long	90	2	¾	•	•				Spring	Summer	
Rye, Winter		No	Widely Adaptable	L		Long	90	2	¾	•	•				Fall	Spring	One of the most important winter cover crops. Can be sown late.
Rye-Grass, Italian		No	Widely Adaptable	L		Long	35	1	¾	•	•	•		•	Fall / Spring	Spring / Summer	An important winter cover crop where winters are mild. In severe climates sow in spring or summer.
Sesbania		Yes	Widely Adaptable	L	•	Long	25	1	¾		•	•		•	Spring or Summer	Summer or Fall	Quick grower. Is better adapted to wet soils and will grow at higher altitudes than crotalaria.
Sorghum		No	Light Loams			Long	90	2½	¾	•	•			•	Late Spring or Summer	Summer or Fall	Do not sow until ground is warm and weather is settled. More drought resistant than corn.
Sudan Grass		No	Widely Adaptable	L		Long	35	1	¾	•	•	•	•	•	Late Spring or Summer	Summer or Fall	Rapid grower. Do not sow until ground is warm and weather is settled.
Sunflower		No	Widely Adaptable	L			20	¾	¾	•	•				Spring or Summer	Summer or Fall	Intolerant of acid soils.
Sweet-Clover	Common White	Yes	Heavy Loams	H		Long	15	½	½	•			•	•			Quite winter hardy. Best results are from fall sowing.
	Annual (Hubam)	Yes	Loams	H		Long	15	½	½			•					A true annual. Best results from spring sowings.
	Yellow	Yes	Loams	H		Long	15	½	½	•	•		•	•			Stands dry conditions better than common white sweet clover.
	Yellow Annual	Yes	Loams	H		Long	15	½	½	•	•	•	•				Most useful south of the cotton belt as winter cover. North not winter hardy. Makes short summer growth.
Vetch	Common	Yes	Widely Adaptable	L		Medium	60	1½	¾	•	•	•	•	•	Spring / Fall	Fall / Spring	Not winter hardy where severe cold is experienced. Needs reasonably fertile soil.
	Hairy	Yes	Widely Adaptable	L	•	Long	60	1½	¾	•	•	•	•	•	Spring / Fall	Fall / Spring	The most winter hardy vetch. Best sown in fall mixed with winter rye or winter wheat.
	Hungarian	Yes	Heavy Loams	L		Long	60	1½	¾	•	•		•	•	Spring / Fall	Fall / Spring	Next to hairy vetch the most winter hardy of the vetches. Not winter hardy where winters are severe. Needs fairly fertile soil.
	Purple	Yes	Loams	L		Long	60	1½	¾	•	•	•	•	•	Spring / Fall	Fall / Spring	Least hardy of the vetches. Suited for winter cover in mild climates only.
	Woolly Pod	Yes	Widely Adaptable	L		Long	60	1½	¾	•			•	•	Spring / Fall	Fall / Spring	
Wheat, Winter		No	Loams	L		Long	100	2½	¾	•			•		Fall	Spring	

Areas For Which Best Adapted

23

Rye between crop rows. Below, a problem hillside.

The chart we have placed on pages 22 and 23 brings together as much information as could be gathered on seed varieties for green manuring. But please don't think your soil improvement plan need be complicated.

Just use this chart as a guide and plant whatever seeds you can, whenever it's reasonable to plant them in temporarily idle ground. The important thing is to get the soil protected and some green matter growing.

5. Plant Green Manures all Year for Maximum Results:

Once you realize and see the improvement that comes from green manuring, you'll try not to let bare parts of your garden waste valuable time during your growing season again. A few weeks after turning under the residues of your early crops, like peas and lettuce, you can help restore the soil's organic matter. Broad strips of annual ryegrass can get a head start in mid-summer, well before the onions and other vegetables are harvested nearby.

Spring

If you'd like a green manure planted in very early spring to improve soil that will be planted later that season, try regular garden peas of an early variety. They produce rapid growth, in great quantity and can be planted as soon in the spring as the soil can be worked. After you harvest the peas and turn under the residues as green manure, wait a week or so and re-seed to your next food crop or another green manure. A problem with sowing other, much smaller green manure seeds early in the spring is that not all will germinate, and many will come along later in summer and interfere with your next food crop. Peas all germinate, so you avoid this.

Summer

For growing a green manure in mid-season, we recommend buckwheat. It thrives in dry, hot summer weather, as its tightly-packed stems shade and cool the ground. As discussed earlier, buckwheat grows practically anywhere and is an excellent way to eliminate the weed cycle. Oats are good, too, if moisture is sufficient, and they're always easy to buy.

Fall

Rye is the ideal fall crop because of its hardiness. You can even plant it in late October, if unseasonably mild, and still get a few inches of green growth. Some cover is better than none at all. The perennial winter rye will survive and shoot up again in the spring, allowing gardeners in the warmest climates up to four full green manure cover crops in one year.

To some this may seem like putting in too much organic matter — that it doesn't happen in nature this way. But just keep in mind that neither does nature attempt to grow such heavy feeders as corn, cauliflower, or lettuce year after year in the same location without equal replacement of nutrients.

6. "Problem Soils" and how best to improve them with Green Manure Cover Crops

There are four basic problems which give trouble to the gardener which he can correct with a continuous program of green manuring. They are: hillside erosion, uncontrolled weed growth, infertile soil, and a basically poor soil texture.

The addition of lots of fresh organic matter is going to help greatly with all four of these problems, and with almost immediate beneficial results for the hillside gardener.

Green manuring takes several seasons to repair infertile soil. You'll probably want to have a soil test to help you judge just how much of a problem this is for you. Here are some of the common difficulties a beginning gardener often has to face.

Sandy Soil is made of very large particles which create too much air space between them. Water and any plant

For sandy soil, try a fast-growing green manure.

nutrients quickly drain away. This type of soil needs tremendous amounts of organic matter to help bind the overly loose particles together into "aggregates." The organic matter helps sandy soil to hold much more moisture for those dry spells. So really any available and fast-growing crop, like rye or peas, is good.

Clay Soil, on the other hand, is composed of extremely tiny particles which pack together. There's often little air space for good drainage and air circulation, so water runs off, washing away precious minerals from the topsoil. Alfalfa would be excellent because it grows well in clay and its long roots help to break up the tough clay subsoil. But again, any green manure will start working right away at crumbling the tight clay and improving aeration.

Hardpan could be any soil type that has most of the topsoil removed, perhaps through erosion or from the removal of all surface vegetation. If it's like concrete, you'd best probably concentrate on hauling manure and other materials to the garden site for one season to attract earthworms and some soil life. If you can manage to break up the surface some, either by hand or by machine, buckwheat is your best bet for getting a crop to grow.

Weeds are not usually much of a problem to get under control each season. Keep in mind that weeds should be tilled under before they go to seed or they will come back even stronger. The toughest weeds, like witch grass and nut grass, simply will need very effective tillage equipment to rip out and shred completely. Otherwise a tremendous amount of hand work will be involved. All green manures, especially the fast-growing grasses and grains, will choke out weeds. Weeds could be indicating deficiencies of plant nutrients in the soil. Green manure should help restore the mineral balance by bringing up elements from below and causing increased soil life activity when the crop is turned under.

Builder's Fill. Very often new homeowners turn to gardening only to find a thin layer of topsoil covering gravel, rocks, construction debris, and a mixture of hard subsoil. The land was just graded and leveled this way by the builder. It may be O.K. for getting a lawn started, but cultivated vegetables are more demanding. The best answer is the same as for most all other problems — plenty of organic matter added in every form, especially green manures.

Rocky Soil. The only advantage green manuring could have for rocky and stony soils would be to loosen and improve the aeration of the topsoil. This would make it much easier to dislodge large rocks. And since green manures increase the tillable depth of the garden soil, over the course of a few seasons of preparing the seedbed and cultivating, you'd unearth a great many small stones. All green manures are suitable for this purpose.

Eroded Hillsides. Wheelmarks and footprints on a hillside garden are just about the worst things for it. Rain collects in such depressions, overflows, then runs down to the next depression, and so on. Soon you've got regular gullies, perfect for washing away your hard-won fertile topsoil and precious plant nutrients. Here's where green manures like buckwheat and Balboa rye come to a fast rescue. You need planty of organic matter tilled in. Also, green manures keep idle hillside garden

Often a crop like trefoil can help wet land like this.

sections actively growing barriers to erosion by holding the topsoil in place.

Overly Wet Land. Drainage may be the problem, and perhaps it will take a lot more than green manures to improve. You might have to use ditches or lay drain tiles underground to draw water from the wet land to lower land. But eventually the addition of organic matter, especially in the form of succulent green manures, will attract earthworms whose burrowed tunnels will help drain off excess water. This type of soil is probably heavy clay, and can be turned into a productive garden with the same suggestions as listed under "Clay Soil" above. Trefoil, for example, is a cover crop that will survive in near-swamp conditions.

7. Start a new garden (or expand the one you have) by turning under the thick sod, then sowing a Green Manure

You have an ideal spot for a tomato bed. It is sunny, well drained, and sloping slightly to the south and east, the directions of maximum sun. And the grass is growing lush and thick. Wherever your best lawn is, often indicates generally good, fertile, conditions for growing fruits, vegetables, or flowers, too. But start in the fall. Sod is slow to break down.

The problem, of course, is getting rid of the sod which is so matted together with those tight roots. A tiller with rear tines is well suited for this job, but it takes several passes, starting shallow and going a little deeper each time. By hand, a spade will at least turn the sod under and break up the largest clumps.

The following spring, kill off the sod completely and quickly by sowing a green manure like buckwheat or rye. It will use all the available nutrients instead of the grass and will choke and cover with shade any remaining sod roots. When the green manure also is turned under, microbial activity will be flourishing, and both the sod and manure crop soon will be broken down all the way. Be sure to leave a few weeks after the final tilling before setting out plants or seeds so that the large infusion of organic matter is well "digested."

8. Many also grow Green Manures to harvest and use as Organic Mulch

You may have all the mulch material you need, in the form of baled hay or straw, but they aren't available everywhere. You may, therefore, want to let some of your green manure crop grow tall, to be harvested as mulching material. This doesn't leave as much green matter to be tilled immediately into the soil, but the stub-

A green manure mulch is perfect for dwarf fruit trees.

ble and root growth add a lot in themselves. Then, of course, later on, when the top growth which you've used as mulch has rotted, you can till that in as well.

Organic mulches, like nice long ryegrass, offer several benefits. Plastics and other inorganic materials often are used for mulching, but they provide no food for the earthworms and soil life. Nor do they help the soil to hold or drain water when needful. Nor do they eventually break down and make the topsoil spongy and friable.

If weeds start growing up through a thick organic mulch, you can lift the mulch with a pitchfork and let it down again, smothering the weeds. Green manure mulches help keep the soil moist and the surface dark and cool. This is how both the earthworms and plant roots thrive.

Green manures will reach way down and retrieve minerals from the subsoil, way beyond the limits of a newly planted fruit tree. As the mulch slowly decomposes, the nutrients will be released gradually to the fruit tree roots at a rate at which they can be absorbed. That's a problem with chemical inorganic fertilizers; they dissolve and drain away, so the plant roots can absorb just a small amount of what's applied.

Earthworms are essential to good growth. There are none in the barrel on the left.

9. The chief allies of Green Manure Gardeners: Earthworms

The most misunderstood animal on earth may well be the ordinary earthworm. Most people associate them with a fishhook, when, in fact, their importance is to you, the *home* gardener.

"The intestines of the soil" one authority calls the remarkable activity of the earthworms. They consume raw organic matter, mix it with soil they also "swallow," churn it over and over with digestive juices in their long, narrow bodies, and break it down into the consistency of coffee grounds. Their castings are, of course, far more valuable to plants than raw organic matter, since the nutrients are closer to a form that roots can absorb. Microbes, rain water, and many other forces continue this job of decomposition, but the earthworm does a "lion's share" of the heavy work.

When you come across soil that has a wonderfully sponge-like and soft texture, well cushioned with humus, chances are that there are dozens of well-fed and active earthworms in every shovelful.

Earthworms eat and *decompose* Green Manure to vastly enrich the soil.

There's nothing earthworms like better than freshly tilled-under green manure, because it's organic material that is still young and tender. Green manure gardeners encourage earthworms by feeding them. In return, the earthworms multiply their channels deep into the subsoil where excess water can drain and where plant roots can more easily reach those hard-to-find trace minerals.

Just how the earthworms can work such wonders is discussed in the August 1968 *Reader's Digest:* "The earthworm churns the earth into rich topsoil by blending vegetable matter from the surface into the ground below, and by bringing mineral-rich virgin topsoil up where plants can use it. Passing through the worm's digestive tract, both alkalies and acids become more neutralized. Earth minerals and chemicals are broken down, enriching the soil with particle nutrients that plants and seedlings can more easily assimilate. Experimenters comparing the top six-inch layer of soil with the castings of earthworms have discovered that the castings contained, in a form that plants can use, five times as many nitrates, twice as much calcium, two-and-a-half times as much magnesium, seven times as much phosphorus, and eleven times as much potassium.

"Subsequently, scientists found that soil's content of actinomycetes — organisms that play a significant role in decomposing organic matter into humus — multiplies seven times as it passes through the earthworm.

"Our amazing friend is as energetic as he is talented. Each mature worm casts up about a pound of humus a year. Since a population of 1,000,000 earthworms in an acre of normal ground is common (seven million have been found), you can figure conservatively that earthworms are producing 50 tons of topsoil a year in each acre of good garden soil."

Unfortunately, most large-scale commercial farmers are hard-pressed to *even begin* to put as much organic matter back into the soil as they take out in harvested crops. Home gardeners, on the other hand, have the chance to lavish much attention on a little bit of land, and develop the lowly earthworm to its vast potential for soil building. This photograph shows clover growth in identical soil, except the one at left contained no earthworms.

10. Tools that are especially handy in green manuring

Either by hand, or with power machines, you've got to have the right equipment to get full benefit from green manures. By this time you certainly see that restoring and building highly fertile soil with green manures involves a lot more work for a gardener than just fertilizing, seeding, weeding and otherwise forgetting his soil. So, you really need help from the proper tools to get this green manuring program to pay off.

Keep in mind a major purpose of green manuring is to get the maximum amount of tender green foliage turned under at the right time in your planting schedule. If you are pressed for time, power equipment will become especially important for you.

The Spading Fork is indispensable for the hand gardener. In the fall you use it to turn under and break up the garden crop residues. In the spring you must do the same with the green manure residues. The tearing and bruising of organic matter *while it's still green* begins fermentation and speeds up decomposition of the materials in the soil. The fork is the key tool.

The Rake is for preparing a fine seedbed. Attempting to grow, cut up, and turn under green manures *by hand* on a plot over 1,000 square feet probably is impractical for most gardeners. As a matter of fact, 500 square feet of green manures would be more than enough effort to do by hand at one time.

Seeders come in several varieties and sizes. When gardening on a large scale, they save money by dispensing the exact amount of seeds recommended. Most of us tend to over-seed, wanting to make sure all space is covered. This slows germination and stunts growth. However, experience should make a good hand-broadcaster out of you.

Rollers are handy after seeding and covering especially loose, rough, and clump-filled soils, so that germination will take place. But for the most part, in well-conditioned gardens, you want to avoid overly compacting the soil. So a roller usually is not necessary.

Mowers are helpful to hand gardeners who want to first cut down tall green manures before spading the stubble and roots under. They'll use the mown stalks either for compost or for mulch. Your ordinary rotary lawn mower usually can handle a few feet of, say, buckwheat. But don't try it on three to four feet of winter rye.

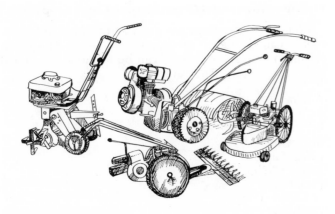

The Sicklebar Mower is, as it looks, a very easy way to cut down and harvest green manures as mulch. Unless you have an extremely large garden, it wouldn't pay to buy or even rent one.

The Scythe, familiar to everyone, is fine for this purpose of cutting down stalks, also. If kept sharp and used properly, the scythe makes easy work of cutting down tall green manures for collection, so long as the area is of limited size. It's a good tool to have around.

Front-end Rotary Tillers were basically designed for cultivating the soil between rows, depending on heavier machines to break the ground initially and to turn under vegetative materials. For many years, they've been the dominant design available. But for green manuring their front-revolving tines just can't handle any green growth without tangling up. If you do use a front-end tiller frequently for cultivation, remember over-tillage is harmful if there's not enough organic matter to shelter and cushion soil life and to form good spongy soil aggregates.

Shredder-Grinders are helpful in combination with front-end tillers to chop up cornstalks, vines, and all garden residues before tilling them in or composting them separately. Most gardeners don't own a front-end tiller and a shredder unless they're growing more than just for summer eating. Shredders are expensive, of course — about the same as a front-end tiller.

Riding Tractor with a drawn tiller attachment is good for gardeners handling many acres, with enough space to allow four to five feet between rows for cultivating. A riding tractor indeed can handle several acres of green manures. The drawbacks include compacting the soil and chopping very coarsely.

Rear-end Rotary Tillers are good for green manuring in gardens from 1,500 square feet up to a few acres. They have powered wheels which drive the machine forward and rear-mounted tines which revolve much faster, chopping, shredding, and burying residues or green manures up to three feet high. They can be substituted

for the front-end tiller and the shredder-grinder combination. Power Composter is another name given to the rear-end rotary tiller because vegetation and green matter is chopped directly into the soil for decomposition, rather than done by hand in a separate compost heap. The value here is releasing the volatile nutrients of the tender, fast-decomposing organic material in the garden rather than in the compost pile where they often leach away.

The Farm-sized Tractor Plow often is for loan or hire in the country if you live near a farm. Normally we advise against heavy farm-size machines in the home garden, since they ruin the fluffy, aerated soil condition you've worked so hard to achieve. The plow is perfect, though, for clearing land for a new garden, provided you complete the soil smoothing and seedbed preparation with smaller tools.

Carts and Wheelbarrows. With a rear-end rotary tiller you can turn all vegetation immediately under. But all gardeners have occasion to cut and collect green manures, or haul organic material like hay, manure, leaves, grass clippings, etc., to their gardens in huge quantities. For this work, one of these extra-large, two-wheeled carts is an excellent investment.

11. Where you can get Green Manure Cover Crop Seeds

Green manure crops are grown from what are commonly called "field" seeds, or farm seeds. The more common field seeds usually can be found at your local farm supply store. They are:

Alfalfa
Barley
Brome Grass
Buckwheat
Cheat Grass
Alsike Clover
Cow Peas

Lespediza
Millet
Rape
Spring Rye
Italian Ryegrass
Winter Rye

Sorghum
Soy Beans
Sudan Grass
Sunflowers
Common Clovers
Hairy Vetch
Winter Wheat

You can order by mail those seeds you cannot buy locally. The catalog houses listed below carry most of the Green Manure seeds included on the large chart on pages 22 and 23. We suggest that you write to all of them and ask for catalogs or price lists which include green manure field seeds in garden-size quantities. When you order small quantities by mail, you should figure that the postage will cost as much as the seed itself.

Earl May Seed & Nursery Co.
Elm Street
Shenandoah, Iowa 51601

R.H. Shumway Seedsman
628 Cedar Street
Rockford, Illinois 61101

Wyatt Quarles Seed Co.
P.O. Box 2131
Raleigh, N.C. 27602

Henry Field Seed & Nursery Co.
5564 Oak Street
Shenandoah, Iowa 51601

12. Keeping your garden soil in good shape with green manures . . .

If you've got enough land, it would be ideal to rotate the growing of food crops with green manures. Then you'll be sure of not exhausting soil nutrients faster than you replace them.

Try different varieties of green manures. You'll surely find some do much better than others. Experiment with a combination of fast-growing grains, or with grasses, or with a slow-growing but nitrogen-fixing legume.

Be sure to keep your garden clean and cleared of crop residues. If you don't have the time to sow a green manure, at least protect and insulate the ground with an organic mulch.

Improving your piece of the good earth, however large or small, is surely one of the best gifts you can make to our environment. What better way to do this than growing *two* crops each year in your garden — a year's supply of fresh fruits and vegetables for your family, *and* a green manure crop to nourish and restore your soil?

We Americans who are so technically advanced might do well to learn the successful steps of soil care from the Chinese who, in harmony with nature, have grown both food and green manures in rotation now for centuries.

We hope from reading this book you will want to try green manuring yourself. One lesson has been proven to us in Vermont: keep your soil and earthworms well fed, and you, in turn, will be amply rewarded.

Hard to beat is the garden nourished by green manures.

GREEN MANURES PHOTO GALLERY

Some additional ideas to help you plan
successful garden soil improving.

Strings help make a straight, wide row of broadcasted peas. Vines grow against each other, supporting themselves without stakes. The yield is greatly expanded with this system of planting, while that many more leguminous peas aid in soil nitrogen enrichment.

Here is proof of alfalfa's ability to penetrate the subsoil in search of nutrients. Roots reach as far as twenty feet. Alfalfa should be allowed to grow for at least two years to get maximum benefit from their vast root system. Meanwhile, the hay can be cut as a most outstanding organic mulch.

Buckwheat — the abundant, fast-growing green manure. Here is how your garden, or a portion of it, can look in just a few weeks after sowing buckwheat. Needless to say, there's no room left for weeds.

It's important to cut down or till under the buckwheat before the formation of new seeds, which would continue the buckwheat's growing cycle the following season. Also, the stalks while green and still tender are more readily available as nourishment for the soil life than if they became yellow and tough.

There is a tremendous demand for front-mounted rotary tillers of this type, primarily for cultivating previously worked soil. However, they can not offer much help to the green manure gardener. Standing weeds and vegetation easily tangle in their revolving front tines, designed for propelling as well as tilling.

Riding tractors are best suited for ground breaking and wide row cultivating in very large gardens with produce for sale. Although their blades are in the rear, the weight of the machine still causes deep ruts from wheels. There is less maneuverability, and as much tendency to tangle up on vegetation as with a front-end tiller.

Shredders come in all shapes and sizes, from the handmade version above to the power-driven wheels model at right. For green manuring, they are used in combination with a front end tiller, or simply a spade, to "pre-digest" material by turning the shredded materials under more completely.

This rented sickle bar mower, or power scythe, is about to cut down a few feet of ryegrass to be used as a mulch. It's expensive, but does a good job of cutting extra coarse stalks and brush.

A heavy-duty rotary mower is often used to chop down residues and weeds as green manures. But unless the vegetation is turned directly into the soil, it dries out on the surface, losing many juices and material which could otherwise have fed earthworms.

A hand scythe, kept with a good, sharp edge, gets plenty of use in a garden being improved by green manures. Here perennial ryegrass is cut for successive supplies of mulch, and will eventually be completely tilled under, roots and all, with a rear-end tiller.

In addition to green manures, an excellent source of rapid soil building is the bringing of large quantities of rotted leafmold and animal manures to your garden. The big two-wheeled Vermont carts make this a pleasant garden project.

The perfect powered machine for green manuring is the rearend tiller, like this Troy-Bilt Roto Tiller-Power Composter. The side of the hood has been removed to show rapid tine action.

The rear-end tiller is more expensive than the types with front tines, but it takes the place of all of the power tools pictured, in terms of garden soil improving.

43

This kale, which survived the winter and now is going to seed, is being easily shredded and tilled back into the soil the Troy-Bilt way. The more green and quick-to-decompose vegetation you can chop and bury in your soil, the more rapidly will you see great improvement in all garden vegetables and fruits.

With food prices soaring, maintaining wonderfully textured, fertile backyard garden soil is among the most important, money-saving activities people can undertake.